Music Theory Practice Papers 2018

ABRSM's *Music Theory Practice Papers 2018* are based on the 2018 Music Theory exam papers. The questions are the same as those used in recent exams.

Find out more about our Music Theory exams at **www.abrsm.org/theory**.

Music Theory Practice Papers 2018

ABRSM's *Music Theory Practice Papers 2018* are based on the 2018 Music Theory exam papers. The questions are the same as those used in recent exams.

Find out more about our Music Theory exams at **www.abrsm.org/theory**.

Theory Paper   Grade 5   2018   A

TOTAL MARKS
100

Duration 2 hours

This paper contains SEVEN questions, ALL of which should be answered.
Write your answers on this paper – no others will be accepted.
Answers must be written clearly and neatly – otherwise marks may be lost.

1   (a)   Look at the following extract and then answer the questions below.

15

Mozart, Piano Sonata in D, K. 284

(i)   The extract begins on the first beat of the bar. Put in the missing bar-lines.   (3)

(ii)   Describe the time signature as: simple or compound   ....   (1)

duple, triple or quadruple   ....   (1)

(iii) Draw a bracket (⌐___⌐) under **six** notes next to each other that form part of a chromatic scale.   (2)

(b)   Look at the following extract and then answer the questions below.

Diabelli, Sonatina in F, Op. 168 No. 1

(i)   Describe the chords marked [A] , [B] and [C] as I, II, IV or V. Also indicate whether the
lowest note of the chord is the root (a), 3rd (b) or 5th (c). The key is B♭ major.

Chord **A** (bar 1)   ....   (2)

Chord **B** (bar 1)   ....   (2)

Chord **C** (bar 2)   ....   (2)

(ii)   Name the ornament in the right-hand part of bar 3.   ....   (2)

2 (a) Describe fully (e.g. major 2nd, perfect 8ve) each of these harmonic intervals. [10]

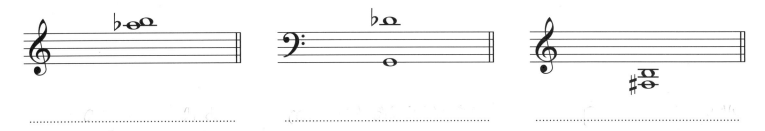

....

(b) **Above** each of these notes write a **higher** note to form the named **harmonic** interval.

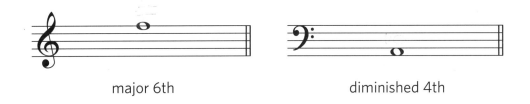

major 6th   diminished 4th

3 The following melody is written for horn in F. Transpose it **down** a perfect 5th, as it will sound at concert pitch. Do **not** use a key signature but remember to put in all necessary accidentals. [10]

Gallay, No. 20 from 40 Preludes for horn

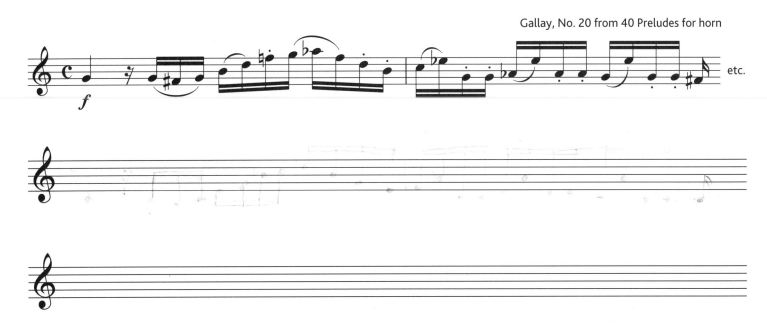

etc.

4 Look at this extract, which is adapted from a piece for cello and piano by Beethoven, and then answer the questions that follow.

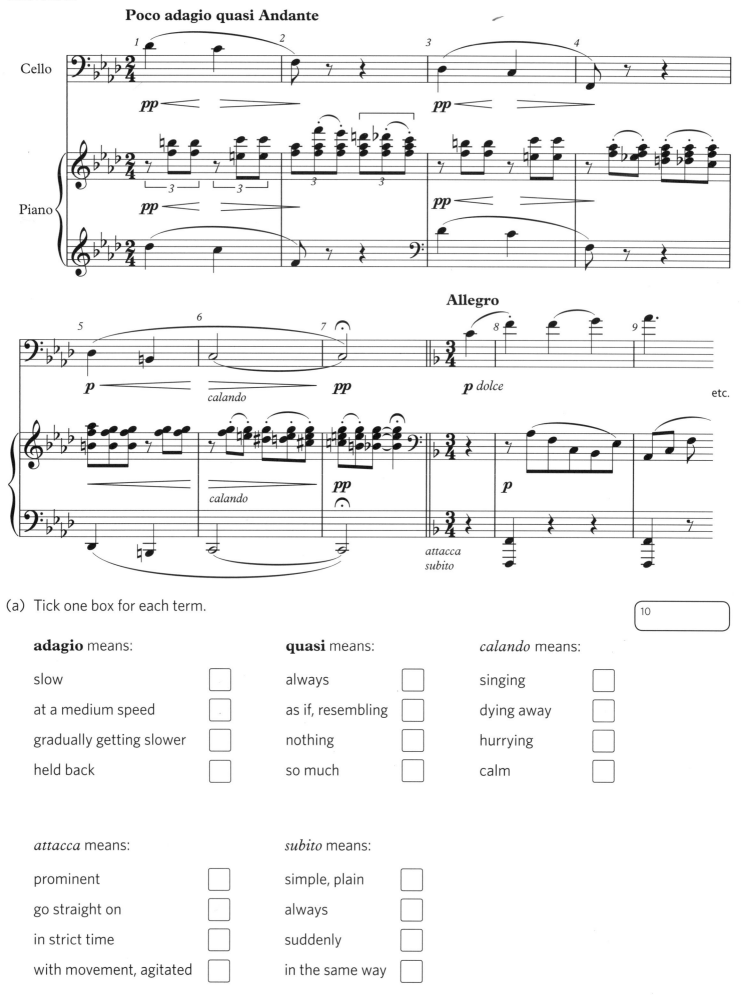

(a) Tick one box for each term.

adagio means:

slow ☐

at a medium speed ☐

gradually getting slower ☐

held back ☐

quasi means:

always ☐

as if, resembling ☐

nothing ☐

so much ☐

calando means:

singing ☐

dying away ☐

hurrying ☐

calm ☐

attacca means:

prominent ☐

go straight on ☐

in strict time ☐

with movement, agitated ☐

subito means:

simple, plain ☐

always ☐

suddenly ☐

in the same way ☐

10

6

(b) (i) Write as a breve (double whole-note) an enharmonic equivalent of the first cello note of the extract.

[10]

(2)

(ii) Answer TRUE or FALSE to this statement:

All the notes in the piano part of bar 3 can be found in the key of F minor. ....

(2)

(iii) Rewrite the cello notes in bar 3 so that they sound at the same pitch, but using the tenor C clef. Remember to put in the clef and the key signature.

(4)

(iv) The triplet ( ) in the right-hand piano part of bar 2 (marked ⌐———⌐) means three quavers (eighth notes) in the time of ....two... .

(2)

[10]

(c) (i) Name a major key in which **all** the notes in bars 8−9 can be found. ....

(2)

(ii) Complete these statements:

The cello is a member of the .... family of orchestral instruments.

(2)

It can be played 'pizzicato', which means ....

(2)

(iii) Name a standard orchestral percussion instrument and then state whether it produces sounds of definite pitch or indefinite pitch.

Instrument .... Pitch ....

(4)

5 (a) Using semibreves (whole notes), write one octave **ascending** of the **harmonic** minor scale that begins on the given note. Do **not** use a key signature but put in all necessary accidentals.

(b) Write the key signature of A♭ major and then one octave **descending** of that scale. Use semibreves (whole notes) and begin on the tonic.

6 Look at the following extract and then answer the questions below.

Mozart, Piano Sonata in C minor, K. 457

(a) Add the correct rest(s) at the place marked ∗ to complete bar 4.

(2)

(b) Give the technical names (e.g. tonic, dominant) of the two notes marked **X** and **Y**. The key is E♭ major.

X (bar 2) .... (2)

Y (bar 3) .... (2)

8

(c) Answer TRUE or FALSE to this statement:

C minor has the same key signature as E♭ major.   .... (2)

(d) How many demisemiquavers (32nd notes) is the note in bar 1 (marked ↓) worth?   .... (2)

(e) Rewrite bar 2 using notes and a rest of **twice the value**. Remember to put in the new time signature.

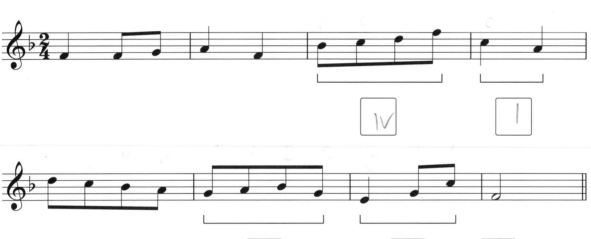

(5)

7 Indicate suitable progressions for two cadences in the following melody by writing I, II, IV or V in the boxes underneath the staves. Use **one** chord per box.

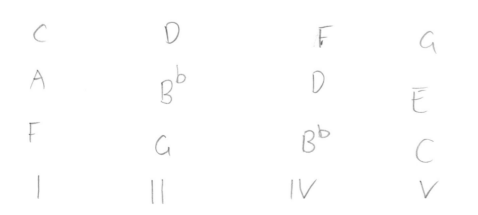

C	D	F	G
A	B♭	D	E
F	G	B♭	C
I	II	IV	V

Theory Paper   Grade 5   2018   B

Duration 2 hours

TOTAL MARKS
100

This paper contains **SEVEN** questions, **ALL** of which should be answered.
Write your answers on this paper – no others will be accepted.
Answers must be written clearly and neatly – otherwise marks may be lost.

1 (a) Look at the following extract and then answer the questions below.

15

Delius, *Brigg Fair*

© Universal Edition A.G.

    (i) The extract begins on the first beat of the bar. Put in the missing bar-lines. (3)

    (ii) Rewrite bar 1 (marked ⌐―⌐) in compound time but without changing the rhythmic effect. Remember to put in the new time signature.

(4)

(b) Look at the following extract and then answer the questions below.

Kuhlau, Sonatina in D, Op. 55 No. 5

etc.

    (i) Give the technical names (e.g. tonic, dominant) of the two notes in the right-hand part marked **A** and **B**. The key is D major.

       A (bar 1) ......Sub mediant............................ (2)

       B (bar 1) ....Supertonic............................... (2)

    (ii) Rewrite the first two left-hand notes of bar 3 (marked ⌐―⌐) so that they sound at the same pitch, but using the alto C clef. Remember to put in the clef and the key signature.

(4)

2 (a) Describe fully (e.g. major 2nd, perfect 8ve) each of these melodic intervals.

.... perfect 4th .... augmented 4th .... minor 3rd ....

(b) **After** each of these notes write a **higher** note to form the named **melodic** interval.

major 6th   diminished 5th

3 The following melody is written for clarinet in A. Transpose it **down** a minor 3rd, as it will sound at concert pitch. Remember to put in the new key signature and add any necessary accidentals.

Cavallini, *Tarantella* (adapted)

etc.

4 Look at this extract, which is adapted from a piano sonata by Mozart, and then answer the questions that follow.

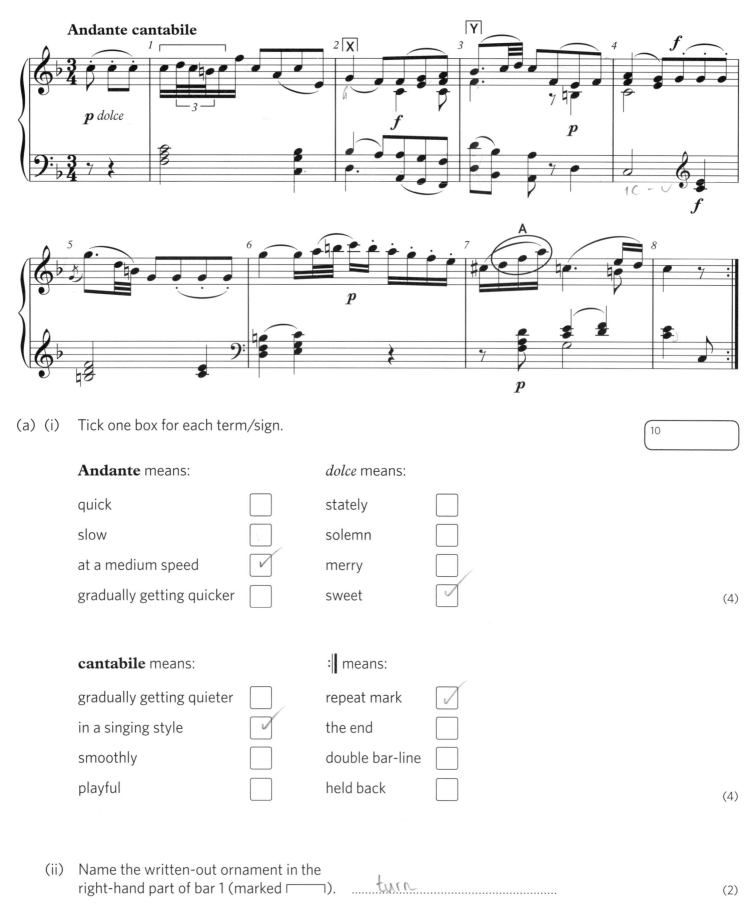

(a) (i) Tick one box for each term/sign.

10

Andante means:

quick	☐
slow	☐
at a medium speed	☑
gradually getting quicker	☐

dolce means:

stately	☐
solemn	☐
merry	☐
sweet	☑

(4)

cantabile means:

gradually getting quieter	☐
in a singing style	☑
smoothly	☐
playful	☐

:‖ means:

repeat mark	☑
the end	☐
double bar-line	☐
held back	☐

(4)

(ii) Name the written-out ornament in the
right-hand part of bar 1 (marked ⌐‾⌐). ....turn.. (2)

(b) (i) Describe the chords marked ⎡X⎤ and ⎡Y⎤ as I, II, IV or V. Also indicate whether the lowest note of the chord is the root (a), 3rd (b) or 5th (c). The key is F major.

⎡ 10 ⎤

Chord **X** (bar 2) .... IIc .... (2)

Chord **Y** (bar 3) .... IVb .... (2)

C	D	F	G
A	Bb	D	E
F	G	Bb	C
I	II	IV	V

(ii) **Mark clearly on the music**, using the appropriate capital letter for identification, one example of each of the following. Also give the bar number of each of your answers, as shown in the answer to **A**.

    A from bar 5 onwards, **three** notes next to each other in the right-hand part that form the tonic triad of D minor (circle the notes concerned). Bar ....7....

    B an acciaccatura (grace note) (circle the note concerned). Bar ...5.... (2)

    C in bars 1–5, a Ic–V ($^6_4$ $^5_3$) progression in the key of F major (circle the notes concerned). Bar ....4.... (2)

    D a note that is the leading note in the key of D major (circle the note concerned). Bar .... (2)

(c) (i) Write as a breve (double whole-note) an enharmonic equivalent of the first right-hand note of the extract.

⎡ 10 ⎤

(2)

(ii) Name a standard orchestral instrument that could play the right-hand part of bars 5–6 of the extract so that it sounds at the same pitch, and then name the family of instruments to which it belongs.

Instrument .... violin .... Family .... String .... (4)

(iii) Now name a **different** family of standard orchestral instruments and then name its lowest-sounding member.

Family .... brass .... Instrument .... tuba .... (4)

13

5 (a) Using semibreves (whole notes), write one octave **descending** of the **chromatic** scale that begins on the given note. Remember to put in all necessary accidentals.

(b) Put accidentals in front of the notes that need them to form the scale of C♯ **melodic** minor. Do **not** use a key signature.

F - C G D

6 Look at the following extract and then answer the questions below.

Poco adagio, lugubre

Sebastian Forbes, *Saul's Blindness*

(a) The extract begins on the first beat of the bar. Put in the correct time signature. (2)

(b) Rewrite the last two notes of bar 1 (marked ⌐___⌐) so that they sound at the same pitch, but using the tenor C clef. Remember to put in the clef.

(3)

(c) Give the letter name of the **lowest** note in the extract. ....*e*............. (2)

(d) Draw a bracket (⌐▔▔▔¬) over **three** notes next to each other that form part of a chromatic scale.

(2)

(e) Answer TRUE or FALSE to these statements:

There are two melodic intervals of a perfect 4th in this extract. ....*true*........

(2)

Langsam has a similar meaning to **adagio**. .....*false*.....

(2)

(f) How many demisemiquavers (32nd notes) are
the tied notes in bar 4 (marked ↓) worth in total? ....*28*....

(2)

7 Indicate suitable progressions for two cadences in the following melody by writing I, II, IV or V
in the boxes underneath the staves. Use **one** chord per box.

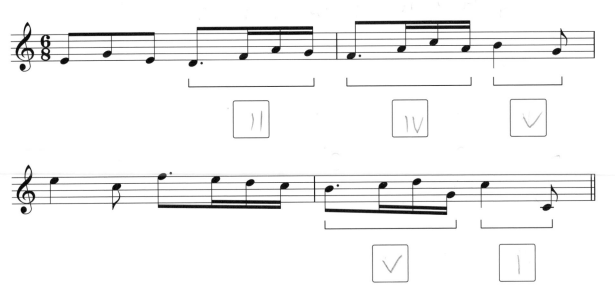

Theory Paper   Grade 5   2018   C

Duration 2 hours

This paper contains **SEVEN** questions, **ALL** of which should be answered.
Write your answers on this paper – no others will be accepted.
Answers must be written clearly and neatly – otherwise marks may be lost.

1 (a) Look at the following extract and then answer the questions below.

15

Bloch, *Schelomo*

(i) The extract begins on the first beat of the bar and contains a change of time signature. Put in the correct time signatures at the **two** places marked ∗. (4)

(ii) Give the number of a bar that contains a note **and** its enharmonic equivalent.   Bar .... (2)

(iii) Rewrite the two notes in bar 4 (marked ☐) so that they sound at the same pitch, but using the alto C clef. Remember to put in the clef.

(3)

(b) Look at the following extract and then answer the question below.

Handel, *Athalia* (adapted)

Describe the chords marked ☐A☐ , ☐B☐ and ☐C☐ as I, II, IV or V. Also indicate whether the lowest note of the chord is the root (a), 3rd (b) or 5th (c). The key is B♭ major.

Chord **A** (bar 1) .... I C .... (2)

Chord **B** (bar 2) .... II b .... (2)

Chord **C** (bar 2) .... V b .... (2)

F   G   B♭   C
D   E♭   G   A
B♭   C   E♭   F
I   II   IV   V

2 (a) Describe fully (e.g. major 2nd, perfect 8ve) each of these harmonic intervals.

.... minor 6th .... major 7th .... augmented 5th

(b) **Above** each of these notes write a **higher** note to form the named **harmonic** interval.

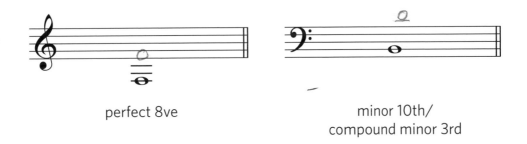

perfect 8ve   minor 10th/
                               compound minor 3rd

3 These are the actual sounds made by a trumpet in B♭. Rewrite the passage as it would appear for the player to read, that is, transpose it **up** a major 2nd. Do **not** use a key signature but remember to put in all necessary accidentals.

Hindemith, Trumpet Sonata

4 Look at this extract, which is adapted from a song by Cornelius, and then answer the questions that follow.

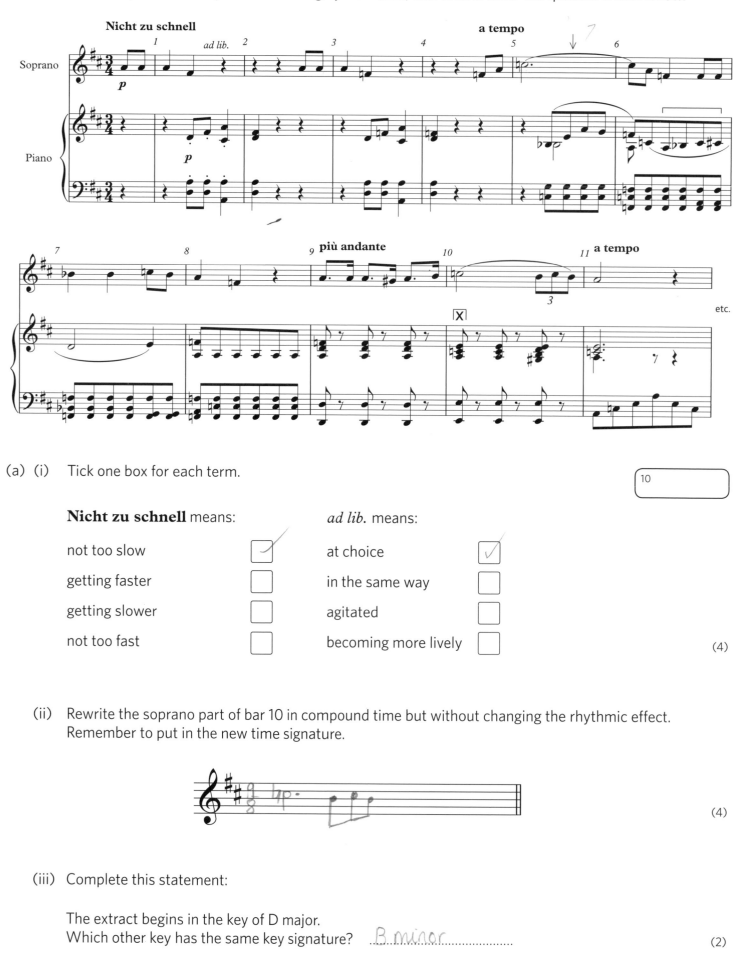

(a) (i) Tick one box for each term.

10

Nicht zu schnell means: *ad lib.* means:

not too slow   ☑   at choice   ☑

getting faster   ☐   in the same way   ☐

getting slower   ☐   agitated   ☐

not too fast   ☐   becoming more lively   ☐

(4)

(ii) Rewrite the soprano part of bar 10 in compound time but without changing the rhythmic effect. Remember to put in the new time signature.

(4)

(iii) Complete this statement:

The extract begins in the key of D major.
Which other key has the same key signature? ....B minor................

(2)

18

(b) (i) How many demisemiquavers (32nd notes) are the
tied notes in bars 5–6 of the soprano part (marked ↓) worth in total? _28_ (2)

(ii) Answer TRUE or FALSE to these statements:

The notes marked ⌐—⌐ in bar 6 of the
right-hand piano part form part of a chromatic scale. _false_ (2)

The chord marked ⟦X⟧ in the piano part of bar 10 is a
tonic chord in second inversion (Ic) in the key of A minor. _true_ (2)

E
C
A

(iii) Rewrite the first left-hand piano chord of the extract so that it sounds at the same pitch, but using
the tenor C clef. Remember to put in the clef and the key signature.

(4)

10

(c) (i) Give the name of the voice part
that is next in range **above** the baritone. _tenor_ (2)

(ii) Name a standard orchestral instrument that could play the soprano part of the extract so that it
sounds at the same pitch, and then name the family of instruments to which it belongs.

Instrument _violin_   Family _String_ (4)

(iii) Name two standard orchestral percussion instruments, one that produces sounds of definite
pitch and one that produces sounds of indefinite pitch.

Definite pitch _timpani_ (2)

Indefinite pitch _cymbals_ (2)

5 (a) Write the key signature of three flats and then one octave **descending** of the **harmonic** minor scale with that key signature. Use semibreves (whole notes), begin on the tonic and remember to put in any necessary accidentals.   Eb   BEA

(b) Using semibreves (whole notes), write one octave **ascending** of the major scale that begins on the given note. Do **not** use a key signature but put in all necessary accidentals.

6 Look at the following extract and then answer the questions below.

15

Reger, Clarinet Sonata No. 3, Op. 107

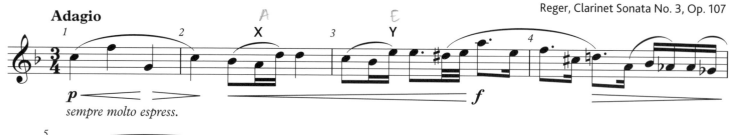

(a) Give the technical names (e.g. tonic, dominant) of the two notes marked **X** and **Y**. The key is F major.

X (bar 2) .... mediant .... (2)

Y (bar 3) .... leading note .... (2)

(b) Describe the time signature as: simple or compound .... simple .... (1)

                                            duple, triple or quadruple .... triple .... (1)

20

(c) Rewrite bar 5 using notes of **half the value**. Remember to put in the new time signature.

(5)

(d) Answer TRUE or FALSE to these statements:

A bassoonist could play this extract so that it sounds at the same pitch.   .... (2)

The largest melodic interval between two notes
next to each other in this extract is a minor 7th.   .... (2)

7 Indicate suitable progressions for two cadences in the following melody by writing I, II, IV or V [10]
in the boxes underneath the staves. Use **one** chord per box.

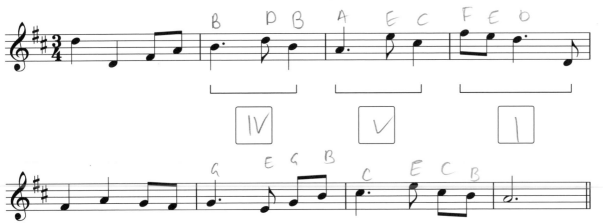

Theory Paper   Grade 5   2018   S

Duration 2 hours

This paper contains **SEVEN** questions, **ALL** of which should be answered.
Write your answers on this paper – no others will be accepted.
Answers must be written clearly and neatly – otherwise marks may be lost.

TOTAL MARKS
100

1 (a) Look at the following extract and then answer the questions below.

15   *15*

J. S. Bach, Cantata *Es ist euch gut*, BWV 108 (adapted)

(i) The extract begins on the first beat of the bar. Put in the missing bar-lines. (3)

(ii) Name the ornament marked ↓.   *mordent* (2)

(b) Look at the following extract and then answer the questions below.

Haydn, Mass in D minor, Hob. XXII/11 (adapted)

(i) Describe the chords marked **A** and **B** as I, II, IV or V. Also indicate whether the
lowest note of the chord is the root (a), 3rd (b) or 5th (c). The key is G major.

	D	E	a	A
	B	C	E	F#
	G	A	C	D
	I	II	IV	V

Chord **A** (bar 3)   *I b* (2)

Chord **B** (bar 3)   *II* (2)

(ii) Below the staves write Ic–V ($^6_4$ $^5_3$) under the **two** chords next to each other where this
progression occurs. Remember that the key is G major. (2)

(iii) Give the time name (e.g. crotchet or
quarter note) of the **shortest** note in the extract.   *demisemiquaver* (2)

(iv) Name the written-out ornament in bar 2 (marked ⌐⌐).   *turn* (2)

2 (a) Describe fully (e.g. major 2nd, perfect 8ve) each of these melodic intervals.
[10] 10

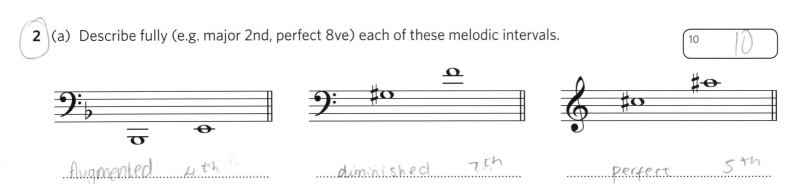

...Augmented.... 4 th ....diminished.... 7 th ....perfect.......... 5 th

(b) **After** each of these notes write a **higher** note to form the named **melodic** interval.

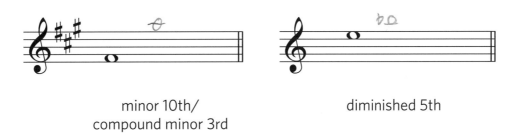

minor 10th/
compound minor 3rd

diminished 5th

3 The following melody is written for cor anglais. Transpose it **down** a perfect 5th, as it will sound at concert pitch. Remember to put in the new key signature and add any necessary accidentals.
[10] 10

Yvon, Sonata for cor anglais and piano

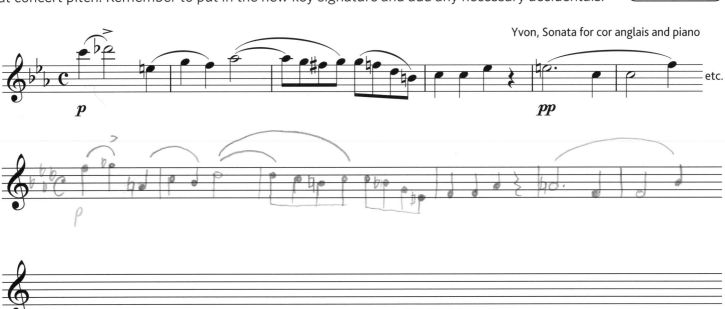

4 Look at this extract, which is adapted from a piano piece by Lemoine, and then answer the questions that follow. **Note that the left-hand part is in the treble clef in bars 1–8.**

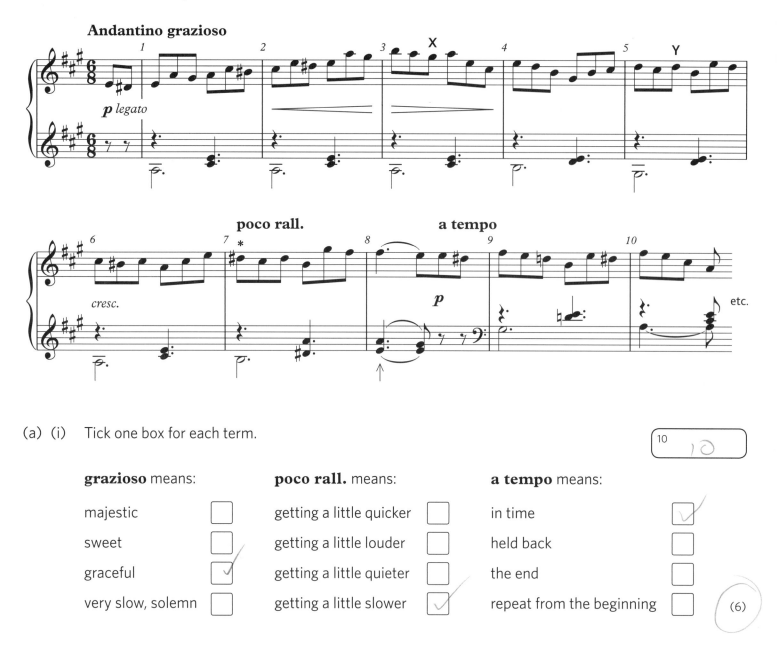

(a) (i) Tick one box for each term.

10

grazioso means:

majestic	☐
sweet	☐
graceful	☑
very slow, solemn	☐

poco rall. means:

getting a little quicker	☐
getting a little louder	☐
getting a little quieter	☐
getting a little slower	☑

a tempo means:

in time	☑
held back	☐
the end	☐
repeat from the beginning	☐

(6)

(ii) Rewrite the first left-hand chord of bar 8 (marked ↑) so that it sounds at the same pitch, but using the alto C clef. Remember to put in the clef and the key signature.

(4)

10 | 10

(b) (i) Describe the time signature as: simple or compound ....compound........... (1)

duple, triple or quadruple ....duple................ (1)

(ii) Give the technical names (e.g. tonic, dominant) of the two notes in the right-hand part marked **X** and **Y**. The key is A major.

X (bar 3) ....leading note......... (2)

A B C D E F# G#

Y (bar 5) ....sub dominant..... (2)

(iii) Complete this statement:

All the notes in bars 7–8 can be found in the scale of ....e........... major. (2)

(iv) Write as a breve (double whole-note) an enharmonic equivalent of the first right-hand note of bar 7 (marked ∗).

(2)

(c) (i) Name a standard orchestral instrument that could play the right-hand part of the extract so that it sounds at the same pitch, and then name the family of instruments to which it belongs.

10 | 10

Instrument ......violin............................. Family ....String.............. (4)

(ii) Now name a **different** family of standard orchestral instruments and then name its lowest-sounding member.

Family ....brass.................... Instrument ....tuba................ (4)

(iii) Underline **one** of the percussion instruments from the list below that produces sounds of indefinite pitch.

celesta   marimba   cymbals   glockenspiel (2)

5 (a) Using semibreves (whole notes), write one octave **ascending** of the **chromatic** scale that begins on the given note. Remember to put in all necessary accidentals.

10   10

(b) Put accidentals in front of the notes that need them to form the scale of G♯ **melodic** minor. Do **not** use a key signature.

6 Look at the following extract and then answer the questions below.

15   10

Finzi, No. 1 from Five Bagatelles for clarinet and piano (adapted)

© Copyright 1945 by Hawkes & Son (London) Ltd
Reproduced by permission of Boosey & Hawkes Music Publishers Ltd.

(a) Tick one box for this term.

deciso means:

delicate   ☐
graceful   ☐
energetic   ☐
with determination   ☑

(2)

(b) Add the correct rest(s) at the place marked ✳ to complete bar 1.

(2)